Literacy
Activity Book

Year 1 Term 2

Louis Fidge

Letts
and
LONSDALE

Every effort has been made to trace copyright holders and to obtain their permission for the use of copyright material. The authors and publishers would gladly receive information enabling them to rectify any error or omission in subsequent editions.

First published 2000
08/051208

Letts and Lonsdale
4 Grosvenor Place
London SW1X 7DL

School orders: 015395 64910
School enquiries: 015395 65921
Parent and student enquiries: 015395 64913
Email: enquiries@lettsandlonsdale.co.uk
Website: www.lettsandlonsdale.com

Text © Louis Fidge

Designed by Gecko Limited, Bicester, Oxon
Produced by Ken Vail Graphic Design, Cambridge

Colour reproduction by PDQ, Bungay, Suffolk

Illustrated by Phil Burrows, Rob Englebright, Sarah Geeves, Graham-Cameron Illustration (Tamsin Cook, Bridget Dowty and Kirsty Wilson), Simon Girling & Associates (Carol Daniel, Mimi Everett and Piers Harper), Tim Oliver and John Plumb.

British Library Cataloguing-in-Publication Data
A CIP record for this book is available from the British Library

ISBN 978 1 84085 448 0

Printed in China

Visit www.lettsandlonsdale.com for free education and revision advice.

Letts and Lonsdale make every effort to ensure that all paper used in our books is made from wood pulp obtained from well-managed forests, controlled sources and recycled wood or fibre.

Introduction

The Year 1 Literacy Textbooks:

- support the teaching of the Literacy Hour
- are best used along with the *Year 1 Poster Packs* and *Teacher's Notes* which provide more detailed suggestions for development activities
- help meet the majority of the objectives of the National Literacy Strategy Framework (when used in conjunction with the *Year 1 Poster Pack* and *Teacher's Notes*)
- are divided into three books, each containing one term's work
- contain ten units per term (equivalent to one unit a week)
- contain one Writing Focus unit each term to support compositional writing
- provide coverage of a wide range of writing, both fiction and non-fiction, as identified in the National Literacy Strategy Framework
- assume an adult (a teacher, parent or classroom assistant) will be supporting the children, reading to and with them, and mediating the tasks
- assume much of the work will be done orally, with written responses expected only as and when pupils have sufficient competence to record them.

Unit number →

Text for reading and discussion →

Key teaching points →

← Text Level activities (purple)

← Sentence Level activities (yellow)

← Word Level activities (green)

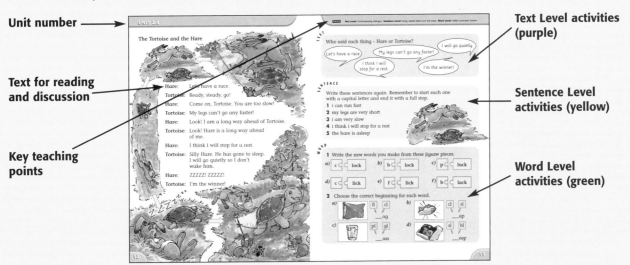

Writing Focus unit:

- appears on pages 26–29
- develops aspects of work covered in preceding ten units
- supports work on compositional writing
- contains support and suggestions for the teaching of different essential writing skills
- assumes much work will be done orally through discussion
- assumes that an adult will act as a scribe, helping children record their ideas for much of the time, and that children will only be expected to record as their developing writing competencies allow.

Phonic Check-up:

- appears on pages 30–31
- reviews the phonic work covered in the preceding ten units
- may be used to provide a review of progress or as further practice in areas of concern.

High Frequency Word List:

- appears on page 32
- contains words that frequently appear in children's reading and writing
- may be used to help children to recognise these words on sight and spell them correctly
- provides an easily accessible resource for spelling and reading activities and a ready reference section.

Focus		
Text Level	**Sentence Level**	**Word Level**
• Features of rhyme/poem	Predicting missing words	Initial, final and medial sounds
• Characterisation	Using capital letters and full stops	Word endings **ss** and **ll**
• True/false statements	Reordering words	Word ending **ck**
• Understanding dialogue	Using capital letters and full stops	Initial consonant clusters
• Sentence beginnings and endings	Predicting missing words	Word ending **ng**
• Recounting main points in order	Predicting missing words	Initial consonant clusters
• Understanding alphabetical organisation	Expecting a text to make sense	The alphabet
• Features of rhyme	Using capital letters and full stops	Segment clusters into phonemes
• Locating and reading parts of text	Reordering words	Initial consonant clusters
• Characterisation	Predicting missing words	Final consonant clusters

Year 1, Term 2

Writing Focus	*Writing about characters; Writing a report; Writing questions; Writing a rhyme; Writing a story sequel*
Phonic Check-up	*Review of Word Level skills covered in Units 2.1–2.10*

CONTENTS

Teatime

I'm a little teapot,
short and stout;

Here is my handle,
here is my spout.

When I see the teacups,
hear me shout,

"Tip me up and
pour me out."

Mix a pancake,
Stir a pancake,
Pop it in the pan.

Fry the pancake,
Toss the pancake,
Catch it if you can!

TEXT

1 What is the first rhyme about?

2 What does the teapot look like?

3 What does the teapot shout when it sees the teacups?

4 What is the second rhyme about?

5 What do you cook a pancake in?

SENTENCE

Find the missing words.

1 M_____ a pancake.

2 S_____ a pancake.

3 P_____ it in the pan.

4 F_____ the pancake.

5 T_____ the pancake.

6 C_____ it if you can.

WORD

Choose the correct letter to fill in each gap.

1 p   c

__an

2 t   n

__in

3 m   l

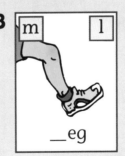

__eg

4 b   x

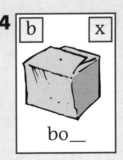

bo__

5 t   g

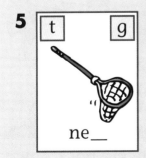

ne__

6 p   m

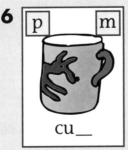

cu__

7 o   a

j__m

8 i   e

s__t

7

Jack and the Beanstalk

Jack sold his cow for some beans.

Jack's mum was cross.

The beans grew into a tall beanstalk.

When Jack climbed the beanstalk he saw a castle.

The giant came home.

The giant went to sleep.

Jack took the giant's bag of gold.

Jack climbed quickly back down the beanstalk.

TEXT

1 Who is this?

a)

b)

c)

2 Why was Jack's mum cross?

3 What did the beans grow into?

4 Where did the giant live?

5 Why was the giant cross?

SENTENCE

Copy these sentences. Begin each one with a
capital letter and end it with a full stop.

1 jack sold his cow

2 the beanstalk grew tall

3 jack climbed the beanstalk

4 the giant came home

5 he went to sleep

WORD

1 Find and write the words ending in **ss** and **ll**.

 a) The giant was cross.

 b) Jack went up the hill.

 c) Humpty fell off the wall.

 d) A snake can hiss.

2 Write the words in two sets – **ss** and **ll** words.

doll	toss	mess	mill	kiss
ball	fuss	well	bell	boss

Foxes

A fox has long ears.

Its nose is pointed.

A fox has a long body.

A fox's tail is long and bushy.

A fox has thick fur.

Its legs are short.

Foxes are wild animals. They sleep most of the day.
Foxes come out to hunt at night.

TEXT

Say if each sentence is true or false.

1 A fox has a short tail.

2 A fox has long ears.

3 A fox has thin fur.

4 A fox is a wild animal.

5 A fox sleeps at night.

SENTENCE

Put the words in order. Remember to begin each sentence with a capital letter and end it with a full stop.

1 short a fox legs has

2 long a fox ears has

3 bushy a fox a tail has

4 wild foxes animals are

5 out night foxes at come

WORD

1 Choose the correct letter to fill in each gap.

a)   a   o

s__ck

b)   e   i

k__ck

c)   o   u

r__ck

d)   a   u

d__ck

2 Spot the odd word out.

a)   back   pack   neck

b)   deck   sick   peck

c)   mock   lick   tick

d)   lock   tuck   rock

e)   luck   suck   rack

f)   pork   pink   sink

The Tortoise and the Hare

Hare: Let's have a race.

Tortoise: Ready, steady, go!

Hare: Come on, Tortoise. You are too slow!

Tortoise: My legs can't go any faster!

Hare: Look! I am a long way ahead of Tortoise.

Tortoise: Look! Hare is a long way ahead of me.

Hare: I think I will stop for a rest.

Tortoise: Silly Hare. He has gone to sleep. I will go quietly so I don't wake him.

Hare: ZZZZZ! ZZZZZ!

Tortoise: I'm the winner!

TEXT

Who said each thing – Hare or Tortoise?

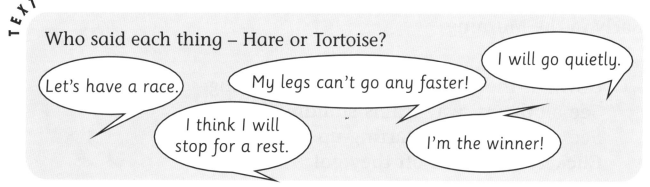

Let's have a race.

My legs can't go any faster!

I will go quietly.

I think I will stop for a rest.

I'm the winner!

SENTENCE

Write these sentences again. Remember to start each one with a capital letter and end it with a full stop.

1 i can run fast

2 my legs are very short

3 i am very slow

4 i think i will stop for a rest

5 the hare is asleep

WORD

1 Write the new words you make from these jigsaw pieces.

a) c) (lock

b) b) (lock

c) p) (luck

d) c) (lick

e) f) (lick

f) b) (lack

2 Choose the correct beginning for each word.

a) 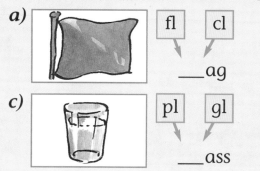   fl cl   ___ag

b)    cl sl   ___ap

c) 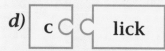   pl gl   ___ass

d) 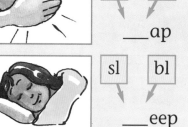   sl bl   ___eep

Early in the Morning

Down at the station early in the morning,
See all the railway trains standing in a row.
See all the drivers starting up the engines,
Clickety clack and off they go!

Down at the garage early in the morning,
See all the buses standing in a row.
See all the mechanics starting up the engines,
Rumble, rumble and off they go!

Down at the harbour early in the morning,
See all the boats standing in a row.
See all the sailors starting up the engines,
Splishing, splashing and off they go!

Down at the airport early in the morning,
See all the aeroplanes standing in a row.
See all the pilots starting up the engines,
Whirring, whirring and off they go!

1 Match these sentence beginnings and endings.

There are railway trains	at the harbour.
There are buses	at the station.
There are boats	at the airport.
There are aeroplanes	at the garage.

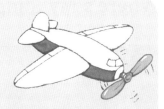

SENTENCE

Choose the correct word to finish each sentence.

boats	**buses**	**aeroplanes**	**trains**

1 The drivers start up the engines of the _____.
2 The mechanics start up the engines of the _____.
3 The sailors start up the engines of the _____.
4 The pilots start up the engines of the _____.

WORD

1 Match the words to the pictures.

sing	king
ring	wing

2 Do the word sums. Write the words you make.
  a) look + ing   *b)* mix + ing   *c)* sing + ing
  d) jump + ing   *e)* stick + ing   *f)* stand + ing

15

Where's My Shopping?

Carra has been shopping for her mum.

"I have some lovely red apples to crunch."

"I have some fresh milk to drink."

"I have some eggs for breakfast."

"I have some sausages for my tea."

"Where's my shopping?"

TEXT

Put these sentences in order.

◆ After this the apples fell out of the bag.
◆ Last of all the sausages fell out of the bag.
◆ Then the milk fell out of the bag.
◆ First of all the bread fell out of the bag.
◆ Next the eggs fell out of the bag.

SENTENCE

Copy and fill in the missing word in each sentence.

1 I have some _____ to toast.
2 I have some lovely red _____ to crunch.
3 I have some fresh _____ to drink.
4 I have some _____ for breakfast.
5 I have some _____ for my tea.

WORD

1 Find a word in the story that begins with:

    a) br   *b)* cr   *c)* dr   *d)* fr

2 Choose the correct beginning for each word.

a) | br | cr |

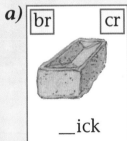

__ick

b) | fr | dr |

__um

c) | dr | tr |

__ess

d) | cr | gr |

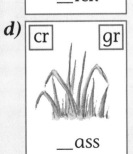

__ass

e) | gr | pr |

__am

f) | tr | pr |

__uck

17

Alphabetical Insects

Aa

ant
Ants live together in a nest.

beetle
A beetle has a hard shell.

Bb

Cc

caterpillar
A caterpillar turns into a butterfly.

daddy-longlegs
A daddy-longlegs has long, thin legs.

Dd

Ff

fly
A fly is a small insect with two wings.

Ee

earwig
An earwig is often found on flowers.

TEXT

1 Which insect comes first in the alphabet?
2 Which insect comes last?
3 Which insect comes after the beetle?
4 Which insect comes before the fly?
5 Which insect begins with **c**?

SENTENCE

Something does not make sense in each sentence.
Write each sentence correctly.

1 Ants live together in shells.
2 A beetle has a hard wing.
3 A caterpillar turns into an earwig.
4 A daddy-longlegs has long thin wings.
5 A fly is an insect with two legs.

WORD

Try this
alphabet quiz.

1 Which letter comes after:
   a) b   *b)* f   *c)* j   *d)* m   *e)* s   *f)* w

2 Which letter comes before:
   a) p   *b)* g   *c)* y   *d)* o   *e)* i   *f)* t

3 Which letter comes in between:
   a) b and d   *b)* q and s   *c)* g and i   *d)* x and z

Clap Your Hands

Clap your hands, clap your hands,
Clap them just like me.

Touch your shoulders, touch your
shoulders,
Touch them just like me.

Tap your knees, tap your knees,
Tap them just like me.

Shake your head, shake your head,
Shake it just like me.

Clap your hands, clap your hands,
Now let them quiet be.

TEXT

1 What is the rhyme called?
2 What do you clap?
3 What do you touch?
4 What do you tap?
5 What do you shake?

SENTENCE

Write these sentences again. Remember the capital letters and full stops.

1 i can clap my hands
2 you shake your head
3 we touch our shoulders
4 i tap my knees
5 it is time i was quiet

WORD

Write the words you make from these letter bricks.

1 a) c → l → a → p   b) s → l → a → p

2 a) s → l → o → t   b) b → l → o → t

3 a) p → l → u → g   b) s → l → u → g

4 a) t → r → i → p   b) d → r → i → p

5 a) b → r → u → sh   b) c → r → u → sh

6 a) d → r → i → ll   b) g → r → i → ll

Mice

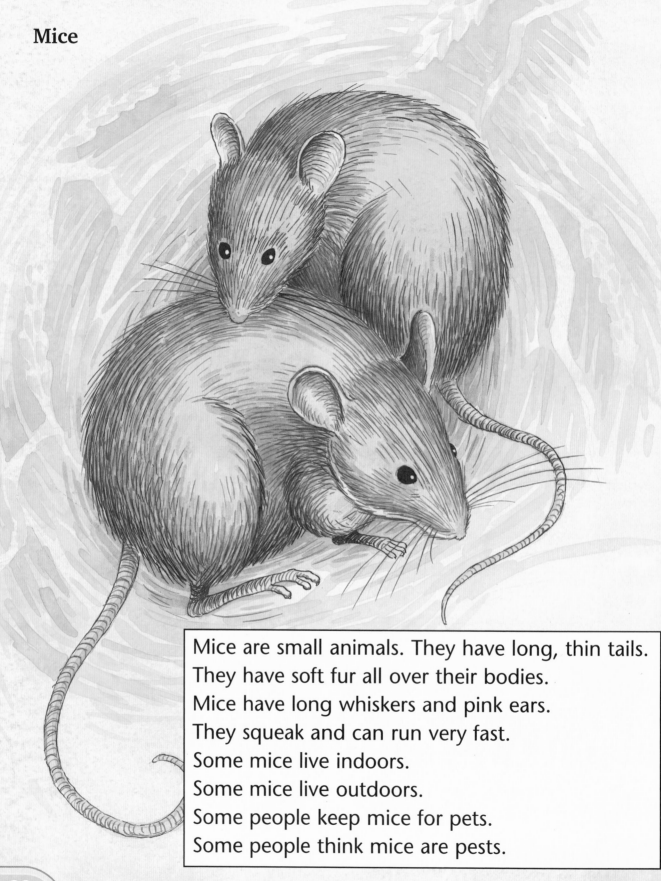

Mice are small animals. They have long, thin tails.
They have soft fur all over their bodies.
Mice have long whiskers and pink ears.
They squeak and can run very fast.
Some mice live indoors.
Some mice live outdoors.
Some people keep mice for pets.
Some people think mice are pests.

TEXT

Choose the correct word to complete each sentence.

1 Mice are _____ (small/big) animals.

2 Mice have _____ (short/long) tails.

3 Mice have _____ (red/pink) ears.

4 Mice can _____ (squeak/run) very fast.

5 Mice _____ (squeak/bark).

SENTENCE

Put the words in order. Remember to begin each sentence with a capital letter and end it with a full stop.

1 mice animals small are

2 soft mice fur have

3 long mice whiskers have

4 mice outdoors live some

5 people pets some for keep mice

WORD

Choose the correct letters to begin each word.

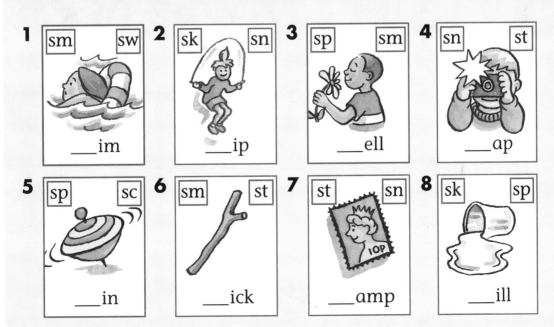

1 sm / sw ___im

2 sk / sn ___ip

3 sp / sm ___ell

4 sn / st ___ap

5 sp / sc ___in

6 sm / st ___ick

7 st / sn ___amp

8 sk / sp ___ill

Grandfather and I

I like going to see my grandfather.
He is never in a hurry. He always
has time to talk to me and listen
to what I say. I love my grandfather.

My mum is always in a rush. She is
always telling me to hurry up and get
dressed or hurry up and finish my
food. My mum is always in a rush.

My dad is always in a rush as well.
He rushes off to work in the morning
and hurries home late in the evening.
He's even in a hurry when he kisses
me goodnight. My dad is always
in a rush.

My big sister is always in a rush.
She says she hasn't got time to play
with me. She says she's in a hurry to
see her friends. My big sister is
always in a rush.

I like going to see my grandfather.
He is never in a hurry. He always has
time to talk to me and listen to
what I say. I love my grandfather.

TEXT

1 Does the boy's grandfather live with him?

2 Why does the boy love his grandfather?

3 What is the boy's mother always telling him?

4 Where does the boy's father rush off to each morning?

5 What does the boy's sister say when she is in a hurry?

SENTENCE

Think of a good word to complete each sentence.

1 I like going to see my _____.

2 My grandfather is never in a _____.

3 My mum tells me to hurry up and get _____.

4 My dad rushes off to work in the _____.

5 My big sister says she hasn't got _____ to play with me.

WORD

1 Match up the pairs of rhyming words.

 nest   band

 belt   wink

 hand   vest

 sink   bent

 tent   melt

2 Make some new words.

   a) Change the **m** in **milk** to s.   *b)* Change the **h** in **help** to y.

   c) Change the **b** in **belt** to f.   *d)* Change the **s** in **sand** to l.

   e) Change the **s** in **sent** to w.   *f)* Change the **f** in **fist** to l.

1. Writing about characters

1 Read Unit 2.2 again.

This is what I wrote about the giant.

The giant is big and ugly.
He is very fierce.
The giant shouts very loudly.
He always snores when he's asleep.

Write some sentences of your own about the giant. Here are some questions to help you.

- Where does he live?
- What does he look like?
- What does he wear?
- How does he walk?

- How does he talk?
- What sort of things does he say?
- What does he eat?
- What does he do after dinner?

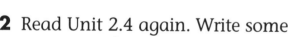

2 Read Unit 2.4 again. Write some sentences about Hare or Tortoise.

3 Read Unit 2.10 again. Choose someone you know well. Write some sentences about them.

2. Writing a report

1 Write about an animal you know well.

Look at Unit 2.9, too.

Look at Unit 2.3 again.

Choose an animal you know well, like a cat or a dog.

◆ Draw a picture.

◆ Write some labels for your picture.

◆ Write some other information about the
   animal under your picture.

2 Write about an animal you don't know much about.

Choose an animal you don't know much about.

◆ Find some books about the animal.

◆ Find out some information about
   the animal.

◆ Draw a picture of the animal.

◆ Write some sentences
   about the animal.

Why not make a class
book of animals?

3. Writing questions

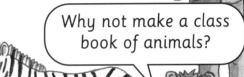

Here is a quiz about
Unit 2.7.
How many questions
can you answer?

1. Which insect has a hard shell?
2. How many legs does a daddy-longlegs have?
3. Which animal's name can you find in
   'caterpillar'?
4. Which insects live in a nest?

◆ Now make up some questions for your own quiz to test your friends.

4. Writing a rhyme

1 **A rhyme about insects.**
Read Unit 2.5 again.
Now read this rhyme.

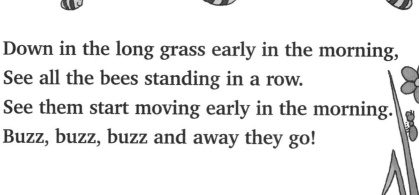

Down in the long grass early in the morning,
See all the bees standing in a row.
See them start moving early in the morning.
Buzz, buzz, buzz and away they go!

◆ Think of some more insects you might find in long grass.
◆ Make up some verses about them like the ones above.

2 A rhyme about your body.

Read Unit 2.8 again.
Change some of the words.
Write your own rhyme like mine.

Stamp your feet, stamp your feet,
Stamp them just like me.

Bend your knees, bend your knees,
Bend them just like me.

Click your fingers, click your fingers,
Click them just like me.

Stamp your feet, stamp your feet,
Now let them quiet be.

5. Writing a story sequel

In Unit 2.6 Carra went shopping. This is what happened:

- ◆ Write your own story about Carra going shopping.
- ◆ Change the things she brought.
- ◆ Draw a picture about each thing that happens in your story.
- ◆ Write a sentence about each picture.

Phonic Check-up

1 Choose the correct letter to fill in each gap.

 b   v   __an

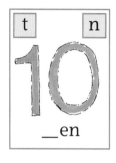 t   n   __en

 g   l   mu__

 a   o   t__p

2 Sort these words into two sets according to their endings.

fuss   pill   hall   pass   bell

mess   toss   doll   kiss   gull

3 Find the odd word out.

a)   **back   sack   rang**

b)   **song   rock   long**

c)   **king   tick   sick**

d)   **hung   luck   rung**

4 Write the words you make.

a)   bl → ot / ack / ess

b)   fl → at / ick / ash

c)   dr → ag / ink / op

5 In the alphabet, which letter:

a) comes after **o**   *b)* comes before **s**   *c)* comes between **v** and **x**

d) comes first   *e)* comes next to last   *f)* comes second

6 Choose the correct letters to begin each word.

sm	sw

__ing

sk	sn

__id

sp	sm

__ash

sn	st

__iff

7 Write the words you make.

a) c → l → i → ff

b) f → l → e → sh

c) b → r → i → ck

d) s → k → u → ll

e) t → r → a → p

f) t → w → i → n

8 Match up the pairs of rhyming words.

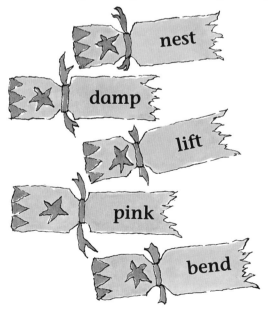

nest

damp

lift

pink

bend

ramp

pest

mend

gift

sink

High Frequency Word List

about
after
again
an
another
as

back
ball
be
because
bed
been
boy
brother
but
by

call(ed)
came
can't
could

did
do
don't
door
down

first
from

girl
good
got

had
half
has
have
help
her
here
him

his
home
house
how

if

jump
just

last
laugh
little
live(d)
love

made
make
man
many
may
more
much
must

name
new
next
night
not
now

off
old
once
one
or
our
out
over

people
pull
push
put

ran
saw
school
seen
should
sister
so
some

take
than
that
their
them
then
there
these
three
time
too
took
tree
two

us

very

want
water
way
were
what
when
where
who
will
with
would

your

Days of the week:
Monday
Tuesday
Wednesday
Thursday
Friday
Saturday
Sunday

Months:
January
February
March
April
May
June
July
August
September
October
November
December

Colours:
black
blue
brown
green
pink
orange
purple
red
white
yellow

Numbers to twenty:
one
two
three
four
five
six
seven
eight
nine
ten
eleven
twelve
thirteen
fourteen
fifteen
sixteen
seventeen
eighteen
nineteen
twenty